CANADA'S ROYAL GARDEN

Portraits and Reflections

NORMAN S. TRACK

with wood engravings by Gerard Brender à Brandis

VIKING
Published by the Penguin Group
Penguin Books Canada Ltd, 10 Alcorn Avenue, Toronto, Ontario, Canada M4V 3B2
Penguin Books Ltd, 27 Wrights Lane, London W8 5TZ, England
Viking Penguin, a division of Penguin Books USA Inc.,
375 Hudson Street, New York, New York 10014, U.S.A.
Penguin Books Australia Ltd, Ringwood, Victoria, Australia
Penguin Books (NZ) Ltd, 182-190 Wairau Road, Auckland 10, New Zealand

Penguin Books Ltd, Registered Offices: Harmondsworth, Middlesex, England

First published 1994

10 9 8 7 6 5 4 3 2 1

Designed by Roger Boulton and Falcom Design & Communications Inc.
Produced by Boulton, Howard & King, Associates
Printed and bound in Hong Kong by Wellprint Inc., Toronto.

Canadian Cataloguing in Publication Data

Track, Norman S.
Canada's royal garden

Includes bibliographical references and index.
ISBN 0-670-85687-8

1. Royal Botanical Gardens (Hamilton, Ont.).
2. Royal Botanical Gardens (Hamilton, Ont.) –
Pictorial works. I. Brender à Brandis, G., 1942-
II. Title

QK73.C22R68 1994 580'.74'471352 C94-930251-1

LIST OF CONTENTS

ACKNOWLEDGEMENTS

The author thanks Barbara Berson, Roger Boulton,
Hugh Brewster, Ellen Eisenberg, Michael Levine,
Meg Masters, Barbara McConnell,
Frauke Voss and Edie Yolles

Canada's Royal Garden

Laking Garden Iris Collection

FOREWORD

by Robert Bateman,
Artist and Naturalist

When we live with a precious treasure we too often take it for granted. The most populous part of Canada has such a treasure and is hardly aware of it: this is the Royal Botanical Gardens. It is a microcosm of Canadian heritage. Wandering the trails or gazing at the views can transport you to a vanished world of First Nations people or the pioneers or the British gentry of the 19th century. In fact, there is such a variety of worlds that you could only begin to relish their delights in a lifetime.

To me it was always a special, somewhat exotic place. As a teenage naturalist in the 1940's I heard stories of Cootes Paradise and Carolinian forests long before having the chance to visit either. I remember standing on the old Lake Iroquois gravel bars, which we called the high level bridge area, with a group of birders led by the legendary George North. It was spring migration and, of course, the end of Lake Ontario was like a huge funnel concentrating the birds into a cornucopia of species. We had the open Lake on one side, the protected marsh on the other and strands of forest and scrub in between. George was rhyming off the names of new birds so quickly that I would often miss two while trying to get my binoculars on one.

One of the best things about the RBG is its strategic location. The end of the Lake, the northern edge of the Carolinian zone, the Niagara Escarpment and the Dundas Valley have all combined to bring about a rich variety of both natural and human heritage. As we reach the end of the 20th century, the most important issue facing us all is the preservation of this heritage. Would that there were many more botanical gardens in every part of the world to help in that preservation.

We are lucky, those of us who have walked the paths of the RBG. As I write this in my British Columbia studio, looking out over the salt water at the mist between the Douglas firs, my own eyes almost become misty as I think about the seasonal richness of that corner of Canada at the end of Lake Ontario. I spent half a lifetime there.

Sharp-shinned hawk

Along the Brackenbrae Nature Trail in summer

Rat Island

INTRODUCTION

by Allen P. Paterson,
Retired Director (1981-1993), RBG

My first experience of a botanic garden was at the age of six, when I was taken on a visit to the University Botanic Garden at Cambridge, England. This visit made a lasting impression; I still remember the green-gold bananas in the palm house. Some ten years later I was back there again, setting out upon a career in which plants have been central ever since. That garden is sometimes referred to as the "Henslow Garden," after its virtual founder John Stevens Henslow, tutor to Charles Darwin. There was an intimate charm to it and I can still remember exactly where so many of the plants were growing, plants that I met there for the first time.

The first botanic gardens, as we understand the term, were founded in the rich city-states of northern Italy, around the middle of the 16th century, and developed out of schools of medicine in the universities that still maintain them to this day. Their function, whether at Pisa, Padua, Florence or Bologna, was to grow for study and precise identification those plants that were of importance to medicine. They were established in an age of intense scientific curiosity, in the heartland of enquiring Renaissance thought. Yet the concept was not without ancestry. In the herb gardens of the medieval monasteries, potions for healing had always held equal place with flavours for the kitchen. As botanic gardens developed elsewhere in Europe, they reflected new concerns of science and economics, and plants were collected from far-off countries.

When, in due course, I moved on from Cambridge to the Royal Botanic Gardens at Kew, the 120 hectares seemed to me enormous, even daunting and somewhat impersonal. Yet here also we student gardeners were immediately given "a charge," a real responsibility for the care of the rare plant collections. I spent a year in Decimus Burton's great Temperate House, then six months each with the tropical ferns, in the arboretum and in the decorative plant nurseries. It was an incomparable way of learning plants.

Being at the centre of a once Imperial and later Commonwealth network of botanical institutions around the world, Kew had long since developed a role and with it an aura that remains unique and whose economic impact has been incalculable. It was Sir Joseph Banks, Kew's first, though unofficial, director who sent William Bligh, the Captain of the *Bounty*, on his first, ill-fated voyage to collect breadfruit plants from Tahiti. It was at Kew that were raised the rubber plants from Brazil which started the rubber industry in Malaysia and Ceylon. At Kew history was all around us.

After I left Kew I spent fifteen years teaching and then linked up again with the botanic past when I took over the Curatorship of the Chelsea Physic Garden in 1973. The Physic Garden was founded by the Society of Apothecaries in 1673 as their teaching garden and has existed on the banks of the Thames ever since. It covers only 1.6 hectares and even in my day was still an amazing anachronism but as rich in rare and historic plants as it was in its legacy of contact with the most significant figures of Britain's botanical history. Living and working there one felt the presence of Sir Hans Sloane, of John Evelyn, of Linnaeus himself, of Philip Miller, of the young Joseph Banks who had lived next door, of William Forsyth and Robert Fortune. Miller, Forsyth and Fortune were three of the nine Curators who had preceded me.

My first encounter with a botanic garden in the New World was on a visit one April to Canada's Royal Botanical Gardens, at Hamilton,

Ontario. So early in the year there was little to see in the way of plants in flower, but I was impressed by accounts of their collections of roses, lilacs, irises, trees, shrubs, and hedges. The desire for a botanical garden had been championed in the late 1920's by the Hon. Thomas B. McQuesten, then Chairman of the Parks Board of the City of Hamilton. He commissioned an elaborate and far-sighted plan for a northern entrance to the City, of which a Botanical Garden was a major part. Royal Assent for the Gardens followed in 1930 and in 1941 the Royal Botanical Gardens, Hamilton, were the subject of their own Act of Parliament and became a Provincial Institution.

Sanguinaria canadensis bloodroot

On another visit two years later, again very early in the year but now as the RBG's new Director designate, I was taken along Patterson Road that skirts the foot of the Niagara Escarpment. Because it faces south it enjoys the first breath of spring. Suddenly I saw growth, new growth, first some yellow coltsfoot daisies. There was nothing odd in this, except that coltsfoot flowers six weeks earlier in Britain. But then, off in the woodland, I saw something white. It was the exquisite flowers of bloodroot, *Sanguinaria canadensis*. This was a flower that I had known in cultivation but never before had seen in the wild. I realized that, hidden within what had seemed to me the sterility of this late Canadian winter, there offered itself a whole new world of wild plants that could capture my interest and devotion. For the next twelve years it certainly did.

Only recently have we come to appreciate the vital importance of conserving plant species in their natural habitats. Over 1000 native plants live on the RBG property. The major parcel of conserved lands is based upon Cootes Paradise Marsh, which marks the northwest boundary of the City of Hamilton. One half of the 480 hectares is shallow fresh water and this and its margins are of great importance: wetlands throughout the world are a highly threatened resource. This same ratio of water to marsh and dryland makes up the linear reserve of the RBG's Hendrie Valley. The Garden's Rock Chapel property, 80 hectares of the Niagara Escarpment, the full length of which is designated by UNESCO as a World Biosphere Reserve, has seasonally spectacular waterfalls and its own diversity of flowers. All of the areas are also remarkable reserves for animals and birds. Towards 300 species of birds have been recorded here.

Cootes Paradise itself is currently the site of one of the most extensive marshland restorations ever attempted in North America. Linked with the Remedial Action Plan for Hamilton Harbour, 'Project Paradise' - as the program is suitably called - is a paradigm for the whole Great Lakes clean-up initiative. The replanting of native plant species and the encouragement of game-fish spawning will combine to produce a naturally self-sustaining ecosystem.

It is often forgotten that not all Canada is a northern land of ice and snow; on the contrary, the RBG lies on a latitude of 43°N, which is to the south of Marseilles on the French Riviera. Though winter temperatures can be fierce, day-length and sunlight conditions compare with the South of France. So, with minimal energy requirements, plants from the Mediterranean littoral and other areas of the world with a similar climatic pattern, hot dry summers and mild moist winters, succeed wonderfully at the RBG. Thus under glass the floras of South Africa, Southern Australia, California and parts of Chile also bring spring to the depth of the Canadian winter.

In the words of the Roman poet Lucretius, *Sic summa rerum novatur semper*, "So the fullness of things is always being renewed." This is certainly true of the plant world. I hope that it may also be true of us to whom that world has been entrusted. For me the greatest gift that the RBG can make to the future history of Botanic Gardens will be to proclaim and instill a respect in Canada and beyond for the natural world of plants on which we all depend.

Rock Garden in autumn

Rock Garden in spring (facing page)

EARLY ROOTS OF THE RBG

by Norman W. Radforth,
Retired Director (1946-1953), RBG

The Hon. Thomas B. McQuesten, first President of the Royal Botanical Gardens, was a man with dreams for his beloved city of Hamilton. For example, the Rock Garden was to be the commanding jewel that would grace the entrance to the city. McQuesten's central and persistent dream was that the RBG should be established as a public treasure, meeting the highest professional standards and fulfilling the best expectations of the international community of Botanical Gardens in which it would take its place.

In 1946, when I had been appointed as founding Director of the RBG, I had occasion to help McQuesten over some rough terrain in the Memorial Garden. I noticed then that he was no longer a young man and I remembered the words of the prophet Joel, "your old men shall dream dreams, your young men shall see visions."

I had known of McQuesten's dream even when I was still only a young lecturer in plant science at the University of Toronto where my mentor, the much revered Professor R.B. Thomson, had generously taught me everything he knew on the subject of Botanical Gardens and I suspect that he had spoken of this to McQuesten.

So I was already open to the McQuesten dream and allied it to my own young vision in a cross appointment as founding Director of the Gardens on the one hand, full Professor and Head of Botany at the rapidly expanding McMaster University on the other.

At that time the word "conservation" was becoming popular in the

The McQuesten Bridge from the Laking Garden

sense of "making wise use of natural resources." I believe that this conception of the meaning was better than our present emphasis on preservation. It seemed to me that preservation, pure and simple, relegated people, visitors, the general public, to the bothersome role of intrusive bogeys. In my view that was totally inappropriate for the Royal Gardens. So far as I was concerned, people would be central to RBG policy, to RBG programs, and to any acceptable proposals for their implementation.

On this topic of public interaction with the Gardens I had the benefit of talking with that widely gifted fellow appointee, Leslie

Laking, who was both Assistant Director and Secretary of the Garden's Board of Directors. We were determined to assemble a membership of supportive people from among the local community. This was a major venture, and took up a great deal of time, but in the end was successful.

We started our first teaching program to meet with the members. They were invited to special lectures and I took care to afford the occasion with a dignity that befit the Crown. Board members were requested to wear formal dress. The Royal Anthem preceded every lecture.

Both the size of the attendance and the attentive response surprised me. Even now I remember how I trembled before I offered my own lecture on plant fossils. Yet membership flourished and grew and especially during the winters we felt the need to satisfy the enquiring interests of our members. So Laking and I were impelled to offer a wider, more ambitious educational program.

Home for the RBG was an old frame building, a former summer hotel of rather questionable reputation. At this RBG headquarters, Matt Broman, the Curator of the Gardens, Leslie Laking and I discussed plans at length. Broman agreed to do some supervisory work among the gardeners who, during the summers, were borrowed from the Hamilton Parks Board. These discussions helped to shape our first horticultural display, a vast spread of spring-flowering plants, mainly prize varieties of iris.

We were not unduly dismayed by the blanket of weeds that in those days covered the Spring Garden area, to be renamed the Laking Garden in 1981. Once conditioned, weed and soil gave way to a landscape of ordered magnificence. From far and wide, people came to take photographs and to learn from the horticultural splendour. The whole presentation exemplified the aims of a Botanical Garden, by its power to instruct and by the grandeur of its beauty. It was also a prime example of conservation in the best, true use of the term, the wise restoration of neglected land for appreciative people.

Meanwhile the chance to blend horticulture with conservation had come around again in the creation of the Children's Garden, which was renamed The Teaching Garden in 1987. The idea was that a patch of land be landscaped and made appealing to children of primary school age. They would need a building where their interests and young skills could be developed. The support of the Junior League of Hamilton made this possible. The children did a superb job and grew yearly crops to show their talents.

At about this time, we felt the need for skilled conservationists with an interdisciplinary approach. None was available, so we developed our own with university help. Graduates qualified in three years, with certification from both the Gardens and the University. Using these graduates as our resource, and with support from the Toronto Anglers and Hunters, we tested plots of wild rice and other aquatic plants in the hope of encouraging the return of migratory birds to our extensive marshlands.

By 1953 my academic and research workload had become much more demanding. I had been at the Gardens for seven years but I was still only forty-one. I decided to retire from the Gardens and devote myself full-time to the activities of the McMaster University Biology Department. However, by stressing research as an essential component of a world class botanical garden, I had struggled to gain the support of the Gardens' Board for research programs, undertaken jointly with the University. These were already fully underway and some important research work on *Ginkgo biloba* had already been completed.

I spent many thoughtful hours envisioning the promised new Headquarters Building. This was to overlook the grandeur of the Rose Garden that was already under construction. For the first financial discussions I made several visits to the Treasurer of Ontario. Only once a token sum had been committed for the Building, could I move on. It was, and I did.

THE TEACHING GARDEN

by Brian Holley,
Supervisor, The Teaching Garden

The first impression that most people have when they visit the Teaching Garden is one of a diverse community of gardens. The family allotment gardens are a patchwork of creativity, cultures and utility. The children's gardens are filled with forts with walls of scarlet-flowered beans, guarded by straw-stuffed scarecrows. The herb garden is flavour and fragrance hidden in silver and grey foliage and splashed with yellow calendulas and blue borage flowers. Apple trees, grape vines and the berry patch give a feeling of abundance to the Teaching Garden. The Plant Lover's garden is set inside a Japanese style palisade off in the corner of the garden. Here there are rare and beautiful plants from the forest, the meadow, the bog, and the mountains. Each environment was created on a scale that can be translated to a home garden.

The RBG's Teaching Garden is located in the Westdale area of Hamilton, approximately seven kilometres from the RBG Centre. This garden was originally established by Leslie and Barbara Laking as the Children's Garden in 1947. They were also the instructors for many years and were assisted by a group of volunteers. These volunteers went on to become the nucleus of the fledgeling RBG Auxiliary. At that time the function was to introduce children to the world of plants and gardens.

While this has remained the primary role of the garden, over the years the activities of the garden have broadened to include adult education, allotment gardening and horticultural therapy programming. Today the garden is really a garden for the community. At the same time the collections and displays of the garden went through an evolution based on two themes, creating a microcosm of the RBG and demonstrating plants of benefit to humankind for food or utility. It became increasingly apparent that the garden was no longer simply for children and the name was changed to The Teaching Garden in 1987.

The goal of the children's programs is to have the participants enjoy and learn about their garden rather than simply develop a knowledge of garden practices. To accomplish this, staff have developed the following strategies: designing the gardens in unusual configurations such as forts; providing the children with a wide choice of flowers, herbs and vegetables; incorporating games, crafts, cooking and investigative studies into the program; and utilizing volunteers to work with small groups of children.

While the Junior Gardener's Club is a bit of an anachronism, it is reassuring that it is still alive and well in a world of video games and twenty-four hour news broadcasts. Many families have had two generations of Junior Gardeners and it is likely that we will have a third generation before too many years have passed.

While it has been recognized for centuries that both the environment created by gardens and the act of gardening are highly therapeutic it has only been during the last few decades that horticulture-based therapeutic, programming has developed. The RBG first became involved with horticultural therapy in 1968 when a former staff member, Ray Halward, developed the Flower Power Program with the staff and patients at St. Peter's Hospital in Hamilton, Ontario. Since that time the RBG has initiated horticultural programs at hundreds of hospitals and nursing homes throughout Ontario. The Teaching Garden staff continue to be active in this area, providing both garden-based programs to challenge individuals as well as training to health sciences and recreation leadership students. In addition ten to twelve special needs groups tend allotment gardens at the Teaching Garden each summer.

The allotment gardens are plots which the RBG rents to individuals, families and groups for the growing season. The RBG provides the tools, irrigation, and advice and the gardeners do the rest. The result is an eclectic community of gardens that vary from dishevelled weed patches to tidy rows of produce to rambunctious cutting gardens.

The herb garden has a remarkable variety of plants, about 200, in a relatively small area. Like other collections at the RBG the herb garden is important as a reference for gardeners but it is also a core element to the Teaching Garden. It provides the theme for the Herb Faire, an annual festival which attracts about 6,000 people. The plants in the herb garden provide materials for craft and cooking projects and are the source for many myths and legends which bring the magic of plants to young ears. Finally, it is a beautiful little garden full of colour, texture, and fragrance.

The Plant Lover's Garden is a little jewel of a garden set in the corner of the orchard. The purpose of the garden is both to demonstrate how a variety of growing environments can be established within a small area and to display superior garden plants in a garden context. The result is a charming blend of tiny mounded alpines in a scree bed, ephemeral flowers and dramatic foliage in dappled shade, exotic bulbs and continuous colour in the sunny borders. It is a garden that demands close scrutiny because every nook and cranny has an interesting occupant.

The little white cottage that is used as a fieldhouse provides a context of the backyard to the Teaching Garden, this special part of the RBG where the growth of people is as important as the growth of plants.

GARDEN AND WILDERNESS, NATURE AND ART

by Douglas Chambers,
Professor of English, University of Toronto,
& Garden Historian

A botanic garden, to the first English creators of such a thing in the 17th century, was a recreation of Eden, where all of Adam's plants, without distinction of wild and tame, might be assembled and flourish. *Paradisus Terrestris* (The Earthly Paradise) is the title of one of the most famous botanic books of the early 17th century, by John Parkinson. And even Milton's Eden was "wild above rule or art."

But the Oxford Physic Garden, England's earliest botanic garden, did not (and does not) include untamed landscape. Even when its rigid layout was modified into the more "naturalised" form that we see there today, wild flowers were placed in tame settings. Not many botanical gardens have succeeded so well as the Royal Botanical Gardens in Hamilton has in incorporating both natures: the elaborate hybrids of rose and iris in the same collection as dogwood, viburnum and jewel-weed; the Laking Garden and the Rock Garden with Cootes Paradise.

Much of what we think of now as wild nature - Dame's rocket (*Hesperis matronalis*), for instance - is only a matter of what has been called "ecological imperialism"; the takeover of European plant types that have frequently escaped from gardens. As we have rifled the

Rhododendron
'County of York'

meadow and woodland for our gardens, gardens and wilderness have become the mirrors of one another, the shasta daisy and the ox-eye are part of one continuum. And there has been hybridization in the wild as well as in the flower border. A Canadian garden is as much a multicultural mix as the people who come to look at it.

From the earliest settlement in Canada, the Jesuits sent back plants to the Jardin des Plantes in Paris, and within a few years of the Conquest the Botanic Garden in Edinburgh was being supplied with seeds of Canadian wild flowers. In the 1790's Mrs. Simcoe lamented that there was not more curiosity about botany among the settlers of Upper Canada. A century later Catherine Parr Traill's *Studies of Plant Life in Canada* (1885) set about to rectify this situation and justified its publication on the grounds that there was "no national botanical garden in Canada, where collections of the most memorable of our native plants might be cultivated and rescued from oblivion." For Mrs. Traill "national" still meant Ontario and Quebec. *Canada's Royal Garden* is testimony to how far, in its short life, the RBG has gone towards satisfying her wish.

But gardening is not simply a matter of famous writers and botanists. When John Evelyn set out in the 1650's to write the first great history of gardens in English, he thought of it as the plan of a royal garden: noble and princely. What he came to write throughout the next half century, however, was an account of gardening that reflected the advice and information of gardeners from all walks of life: men and women who came to be called the "patriots of horticulture."

Peter Collinson, an amateur botanist who imported more than forty new species of plants into England in the 18th century, regretted that the effect of Linnaeus's botanical system would be that only professors would be able to understand horticulture. Fortunately he was wrong. Gardens are the democrat's academy. There the learned and the amateur mix as freely as the wild and tame species and the questions it raises are infinite.

What, for example, raises the question of man's relation with nature more than a garden? One of the best-known garden poems in English is Andrew Marvell's "The Garden," a poem in which the late 17th century poet recognises the power of the mind to annihilate "all that's made to a green thought in a green shade." In his longer poem, "Upon Appleton House," he takes the even more momentous step (for the first time in English) of walking out of what had been regarded as the garden (the formal beds around the house) and recognizing that the landscape as a whole is also a garden.

Landscape is itself a word derived from painting. Indeed originally "landscape" meant only what we now call "a landscape painting," and the poet Pope thought of gardens only as "a landscape hung up" (i.e. a painting translated into nature). The first garden writer in English, Sir Henry Wotton, praised the gardens of his friend Sir Henry Fanshawe, for being "a piece not of Nature, but of art" because the flowers were so planted that the darker colours on the inside of the bed seemed to give a shadow to the rest.

But even a wild garden is an artifice. Even a woodland glade carpeted with trilliums or a fencerow bright with bloodroot and dog-tooth violets strikes us because art has trained our eyes to see it as a thing of beauty. No one who has ever used a camera can be unaware how focus and field create the subject one is looking at by exclusion and enlargement.

The very words we have for these flowers are dense with medical, literary and cultural associations: emblematic, symbolic, magical. Think of the names of *Eupatorium* (Joe-Pye weed), one of the loveliest of our autumn plants. They read like a litany of use and pleasure: gravel root, trumpet weed, kidney root, king or queen of the meadows, skunk weed, marsh milkweed, quillwort. "For my part," wrote the Romantic poet, John Clare, "I love to look on nature with a poetic feeling which magnifys the pleasure... the man of taste looks on the little Celandine in Spring and mutters in his mind some favourite lines favourite lines from Wordsworth's address to that flower. He never sees the daisy without thinking of Burns."

We have a language of botany and a language of sentimentality, but not a language of feeling that acknowledges that large part of our cultural history that comes from being within the nature that we inhabit and knowing it as intimately as a lover. For the early 20th century American poet, Wallace Stevens, the greatest poverty was to live in the poverty of the real, and he represented the ghosts of people who had lived that way as desiring to return to earth to shiver in the frost or run their fingers over the most coiled thorn. Even in the 18th century, that supposed "age of reason," a man like Pope could acknowledge the "delicious feeling at the heart," that a friend's landscape garden could excite in him.

Why do such sentiments embarrass us? Perhaps our problem in southern Ontario is that most of our landscape is neither picturesque nor sublime but beautiful. These are the three categories of late 18th century taste, but by the time of settlement here the beautiful (as represented by the landscapes of Capability Brown, for example) had become unfashionable.

In the face of a vast continent and an intractable wilderness, it is not surprising that the sublime and the picturesque were the categories used to talk about nature and landscape by our early travellers and explorers. And yet the landscape that was created by clearing and settlement in Southern Ontario was neither. It was gently varied, smooth and muted: all the things that Edmund Burke had identified as properties of the beautiful in his famous *Essay on the Sublime and Beautiful* (1757). Moreover beauty was associated not with solitary terror of the wilderness but with human society.

We have created a nature outside of ourselves (the far north, the open west, etc.) at the expense of being able to see where we are and

Along the Bridle Nature Trail
in winter

at the expense of a whole range of feelings and perceptions that have to do with the small and immediate. The landscape of where we are is the landscape painted by Homer Watson, George Reid and C.W. Jefferys and photographed by Reuben Sallows, the landscape of the poets Archibald Lampman and Bliss Carman, the nature of the writing of Ernest Thompson Seton or Thoreau Macdonald. Since the Group of Seven and the exaltation of northern landscape, however, the beautiful has had short shrift with us, and so we have not sufficiently appreciated the woody helenium or the touch-me-not of the wetlands, let alone the cultivated woodland trails and agricultural margins that are our own familiar landscape.

The loss is a diminution in our vocabulary of seeing. We see only what we have the visual vocabulary to see. The hedge garden in the Arboretum at the RBG teaches us to see the white pine as a hedge of feathers and not simply as the giant of Ontario forest trees. The author of the first Canadian botany, Jacques Cornut, Keeper of the Jardin des Plantes in Paris, had never seen a trillium. He had no way of placing it and thought it must be a nightshade. On the other hand for him, and for French culture, the iris was a more potent flower than it is for the rest of the world, symbolically associated as it was with the fleur de lis: the flower of medieval French chivalry.

Gardens are also places of withdrawal whether for love or meditation (the two have more in common than is often recognised), as they have been since antiquity. The wedding parties in the rose garden and the lovers in Cootes Paradise are part of a tradition that stretches back to the enclosed garden of the Song of Songs and the hanging gardens of Babylon on the one hand and the great sylvan academies and Augustan philosophical gardens of antiquity on the other.

Garden and wilderness speak to us both of great happiness and of the lost Eden of childhood: that world so powerfully conjured up by Frances Hodgson Burnet in *The Secret Garden* and celebrated by T.S. Eliot in *The Four Quartets*:

Footfalls echo in the memory
Down the passage we did not take
Towards the door we never opened
Into the rose-garden.

The rose may be the symbol of eternity, as it is in the great medieval rose windows and in *The Four Quartets*, but it is also mortal. "O rose, thou art sick," Blake writes. And the daffodil, that symbol of spring's resurrection, is also the flower that Proserpina was gathering when (in Milton's ominous description of Eve) she "by gloomy Dis was gathered, which cost Ceres all that pain to seek her through the world."

Death is the mother of beauty, the maker of arcadïas, because of our need for a myth of permanence in a world in which we are transient. "This body was taken from his mates and died," Wordsworth wrote of his own lost childhood in "The Prelude": a recognition of the irrecoverability of the child's immediate sense of the natural world and yet our intense need to recover it. It is the Latin theme, *carpe diem* (gather ye rosebuds) reworked autobiographically in the landscape of the Lake District, as we have reworked it in our own climate. "Not in Utopia, subterranean fields, or some secluded island heavens knows where," Wordsworth wrote also in "The Prelude," "but in the very world that is the world of all of us, the place where in the end we find ourselves or not at all."

Gardens, of whatever kind, are where we find ourselves when once we have the leisure or necessity or occasion to begin looking. And Keats was right to suggest - long before Thoreau in America - that this process involves "negative capability," an escape from the world of naming and possession that he called "an irritable reaching after fact." For him this escape was a death to the self that was to be embraced (in an almost Biblical sense): one in which we might find ourselves by losing our patriarchal minds and letting sensation tell us what the botanical handbooks cannot. There we might be happy to be (at least initially) at eye level with the flower's intricacies as Gerard Brender à Brandis is in many of his engravings.

"Men come to build stately, sooner than to garden finely," Sir Francis Bacon wrote, "as if gardening were the greater perfection." But there is an even greater perfection that one of Bacon's contemporaries, a practical gardener called William Lawson, noted in his *A New Orchard and Garden* (1618): that woodland was part of the garden experience. Originating in the Renaissance Italian idea of the *boschetto* (or "little wood"), it became the staple of many 17th century gardens as "the wilderness." But even it was no wilderness in the sense that we use the term: a place untouched by man.

We know that there is no such place; even the Arctic Ocean contains our refuse. But we need to believe in its possibility, the "other," the blank page still unscribbled on by the interfering world of our everydays. True gardens offer us the dialogue between these possibilities: the created secret perfect place and the wild untutored one, both of them part of our definition of ourselves. It was after all within the rigid discipline of a conventional poem that Yeats celebrated the chestnut tree as a "great-rooted blossomer," rooted and yet free, dancing it seems and yet to a rhythm we can never know. It is *we* who make these associations, what Shakespeare's contemporary, Ben Jonson, called "being understanders," not mere spectators.

Rosa × *alba* 'Chloris'

Spring

A GARDEN CALENDAR

by Gerard Brender à Brandis,
Wood engraver and Bookwright

On a February morning, when the snow seems to blanket everything except a few stretches of fast flowing water in the creek, one looks less at the ground, more upwards, up at the sepia and grey oak bark set against the greens of spruce, pine and cedar, at the thickets of red-barked dogwood among the ochres and russets of cattails, and further up to the reddening twigs of birch and maple against the blue of sky. There may just be some mosses on the south sides of large escarpment rocks showing a hint of plumpness in response to the increasing light and a suggestion of warmth in the sun's rays. But one knows that, waiting under the snow, under one's very foot, are the pointed shoots of a thousand plants, patiently waiting for the signal to begin the annual march upwards. The birds are winter's flowers; chickadees and nuthatches, grosbeaks and woodpeckers (the huge pileated one, if one is lucky), perhaps a grouse, always sparrows in variety and number. The brightest of all is the male cardinal, and just one of those cheers up the whole valley.

In March the sugar bush at Rock Chapel comes alive with hundreds of brightly clad visitors to the shack where wood fires turn maple sap into syrup, toffee and sugar. But apart from the din there are subtle

Summer

changes going on in nature. Dark streaks in the ice on Cootes Paradise signal a move to opening of the water. More spectacular are the yellow blooms of the *Hamamelis* in Spicer Court, where the warmth of the buildings and the south facing exposure combine to form a microclimate in advance of all the rest. With any luck the earliest bulbs - snowdrops, *Eranthis* and *Iris reticulata* will be showing colour before the end of the month. But once inside the Mediterranean Garden under glass, one finds the flowering season in full swing. The scarlet stamens of *Feijoa sellowiana* contrast with its grey sepals, *Alyogyne huegelii* is massed with pleated funnels of lilac, hippeastrums and passion flowers overload their plants and the coral shuttlecocks of *Abutilon* weigh down their twigs. The coffee tree in its huge tub holds cascades of berries nearly ripe. And on a certain weekend one finds the RBG Centre crowded to the walls with the annual orchid show - thousands of blooms and nearly as many admirers.

April is the month of bulbs. In Spicer Court clutches of *Chionodoxa*, miniature narcissus and *Crocus sieberi* open in raised beds. As the season advances more and more varieties flower in beds from the Laking Garden to the hollow of the Rock Garden. The nature trails are now coming alive with bloodroot and jack-in-the-pulpit, foam flower, skunk cabbage and the glorious trilliums. Some of the less spectacular flowers are the most charming; hepatica, bellwort, toothwort and the unfurling fronds of *Caulophyllum thalictroides* which are exactly the colour of ripe Concord grapes. Every pond and bend of stream now has its resident pair of mallards. Redwing blackbirds cling to last year's cattails and flash their epaulettes of yellow and scarlet. The maple twigs are red with myriad tiny flowers, while catkins dangle from hazel, willow and aspen.

Even though there may still be a risk of night frosts in May the season of bloom presses on without heed. Ranks of tulips shout at each other from one wall of the Rock Garden to the other. The first pansies have been planted out. In the arboretum the cherries and crabapples are hung in shades of pink. Later in the month the lilac dell is misted in all the tones of mauvy blue, purple, wine and white. Flaming azaleas and rhododendrons decked out in Victorian hues bridge the end of May to early June. But before we leave May-month, remember to notice the arcs of bleeding hearts, crowds of violets among the paving stones, and pine flowers cascading pollen.

June means irises, dwarf, medium and tall bearded ones in spectacular array in the Laking Garden, but elsewhere too - *Iris laevigata* in the Rock Garden and the wild yellow flags along the water's edge. The tree peonies shake out their amazing flowers and herbaceous peonies struggle to support their pink cushions. Flights of columbines take off from the perennial beds and the clematis overflow, some with flowers hanging like little upside down tulips and others like six-pointed stars. Almost every day has a "first," the first poppy, the first lily, the first delphinium, the first rose - a parade that pours from June into July.

There is too much to be said about the midsummer months. Lilies and day-lilies and water lilies in perfumed profusion, trial gardens full of annuals from ageratum to zinnia, the Medicinal Garden full of plants with quaint medieval names and the Scented Garden living up to its name. The roses begin to spill their satin petals carelessly on the ground, knowing that they can open flowers anew each day. The daisy-like flowers gain in prominence; heleniums and gaillardias, cosmos and heliopsis, rudbeckias and asters and echinaceas. After this riot one longs for a walk in the shaded woodland where the ferns and hostas bathe the eyes with subtle greens, or along the edge of the wetlands, where water laps among swaying reeds and a painted turtle dozes under his sun-warmed carapace.

One cannot go far into September without receiving a warning that the season will soon draw to a close. The tall, ornamental grasses push out their plumes, bumblebees rush around the touch-me-nots with unusual urgency, and Michaelmas daisies (both cultivars in perennial

Autumn

beds and their wild cousins of field and woodland) open their myriad discs. There are berries now on the viburnums, hips on many shrub roses, hard, wine-red fruit on the crabapple trees. Monarch butterflies prepare for their long migration by sipping nectar wherever they can find it, grackles start to move in flocks and the ducks blend their families into tribes. Touching the seed-head of an opium poppy in the Medicinal Garden produces a sinister rattle and breathing in the scent of a late sweet pea calls up a pang of nostalgia - another summer gone, and months before a new generation of sweet peas will perfume the air.

So often October revives the spirits with a resurgence of colour. Monkshood blooms electric blue, yellow fumitory blows anew, colchicums and saffron crocus mimic spring with amazing verisimilitude, as does an occasional primula in a moist spot. Tiny *Cyclamen hederifolium* nods under the low, berried twigs of *Cotoneaster dammeri*. The colours of chrysanthemums in tubs and planters are quickly echoed in identical hues by the trees above.

A November walk usually means a heavier jacket and stouter shoes. In the mornings the ground may feel hard with frost. The low, slanting sun lights up the sides of tree trunks, enlivening green algae shaded into oblivion during the leafy months. Even though the eyes continue to scan the landscape for the last delights of Nature's feast the memory is busy storing away all the impressions of the fading year, sifting, blending and comparing with those of other years. Now is the time for looking inward, for assessing one's inner growth, as bare trees draw their sap into their roots, preparing for the long, quiet wait until the planet tilts us sunward for another season.

Along the Bridle Nature Trail in winter

Iris 'Valour'

Magnolia × soulangiana 'Norbertiana' Norbert saucer magnolia

Magnolia × soulangiana 'Saucer' magnolia (facing page)

Crocus 'Pickwick'

Prunus × yedoensis 'Ivensii' Ivens Yoshino cherry

What came with the Roses? Sweet hopes springing forth
'Mid the sunbeams of heaven, the blossoms of earth,
And the song of the birds, and the breath of the flowers
Awakening a dream of life's sunniest hours....

Anon.

Rosa × paulii 'Rosea'

PLANT ARCHITECTURE AND ITS DIVERSITY

by Ann Milovsoroff,
Landscape Architect, RBG

From single cell algae in the marsh of Cootes Paradise to the complex architecture of a 30 metre tall European copper beech or Chinese ginkgo at the Rock Garden there are an astonishing variety of plant forms at the RBG. Each plant is both related to and unique from the others. Evolution has produced some strange and wonderful forms. Considering the vastly different climates and habitats around the world this is no surprise.

Plants are unique among earth's organisms in their ability to convert energy from light, and the life of the planet depends on this ability. Originally emerging from the same watery habitat as other primitive living organisms, plants adapted structurally to the unsupporting air, to extremes of temperature, and to the need to search for water and nutrients.

Most plants use leaves to collect and process the energy from light into starches and sugars, while others may use stems, trunks, or other "body parts" to do the job. Leaves may be measured in millimetres or in metres. Small leaves are usually a response to dry or cold conditions, while large leaves are usually found in shaded, warm, moist environments. Some ferns and orchids grow in the air (epiphytes) to catch the dappled light near the top of dense jungle, while climbers stretch out long stems to reach that same light. In the Arctic most plants have adapted to wind and cold by creeping along

Cleome hasslerana 'Purple Queen' spider flower

the ground or growing as cushions for self-protection. In dry areas plants develop root systems that extend very deep or wide, and have narrow or waxy or hairy leaves adapted to lose as little moisture as possible. The leaves may be silvery in colour to reflect the sun's heat. Cacti and spurges have developed stems that function as barrels to hold water - an example of plants with very different ancestors evolving into outwardly similar forms to cope with similarly arid environments. Tree trunks range in height from a metre to a coast redwood living in northern California that measures 112 metres. Flowers vary in size from a fraction of a millimetre for pond duckweed to the metre diameter of one species of *Rafflesia*.

Less noticeable but perhaps more remarkable are the internal construction and metabolism of plants. There is the complex structural engineering that, cell by living cell, creates a 112 metre upright structure that can sway with storm winds, and whose internal plumbing produces the intricate network and tremendous force needed to move water and minerals throughout every part of that great height, and transport the products of photosynthesis to all parts of the plant. The interiors of plants are the most sophisticated chemical laboratories in the world, manufacturing organic compounds that humans depend upon, but most of which we as yet have no idea how to make.

The purpose of flowers is to attract other beings, usually moving ones, to accomplish fertilization, thereby enhancing genetic diversity. Smelling a flower may dislodge pollen onto the pistil and effect fertilization. Smelling two flowers may transfer pollen from one to the other and result in cross-pollination. The diverse variety of architecture in plants is aimed at successful survival for reproduction. In flowers, it is aimed at accomplishing that reproduction. The architecture is created by the number, size and design of the sepals, petals, pistils and stamens. These, combined with colour, scent and nectar, have evolved in an arrangement that is most likely to attract the visitor (and pollen transferer) of choice.

Bees are particularly attracted by yellow or blue flowers that have an elongated, hollow shape. The face on a pansy, the yellow eye on a forget-me-not, the freckles on a foxglove, are all signposts to the sweet spot of nectar. Flowers such as mints have a strong or enlarged lower "lip" to act as a landing pad. Bees are also attracted by scent, while hummingbirds are not. Hummingbirds prefer red flowers, which, except for the blue-reds, bees can't see. Red flowers that are tubular and held horizontally are particularly attractive to hummingbirds. Their long, delicate, curving beaks and tongues are adapted to probing deeply into the flower. Flowers pollinated by moths are usually white or cream and scented; often opening at dusk. Butterflies, those "flowers of the air" are often scented themselves, and are attracted to similar scents in flowers. These flowers are built as wider landing platforms, facing upward with spreading petals, or as clustered heads of small flowers.

Some of this diversity is displayed in the World of Botany Garden at the RBG. The variety of plant forms, of pollination, and of seed dispersal; plants from the four continents that have become common inhabitants in home gardens; plants that are used for food, medicine, flavouring, and for ornament; non-flowering plants; flowering plants grouped in their families and those families in their sub-classes; these arrangements of plants that make visible the science of botany have resulted in an unexpectedly beautiful garden with a story to tell. In microcosm this is the definition of the Royal Botanical Gardens.

Jeffersonia diphylla twinleaf

Magnolia stellata 'Centennial'

Nature is full of genius, full of the divinity; so that not a snowflake escapes its fashioning hand.

Henry David Thoreau
Journals, 1856

Syringa vulgaris 'Mount Baker' lilac

Syringa vulgaris 'Rochester' lilac (left)

Syringa vulgaris 'Krasavitsa Moskvy' 'Pride of Moscow' lilac (facing page)

Rudbeckia laciniata 'Autumn Sun'
green-headed coneflower

LINNAEUS AND BINOMIAL NOMENCLATURE

by James S. Pringle,
Taxonomist and Research Associate, RBG

By modern standards, Renaissance and earlier European botanists described relatively few species of plants. They were acquainted only with the plants of Europe and the Mediterranean region, and generally concentrated on those of distinctive appearance and/or utilitarian significance. By the 17th century, however, introductions of plants from distant parts of the world drastically altered European scholars' concepts of the world's biodiversity.

Many useful plants had long been known by familiar, one-word names, such as "apricot" and "tarragon" in English. For many of the thousands of species that had been recognized by the 17th century, however, there were no familiar names. In other cases such names did not distinguish among similar species. One helpful development was the concept of the genus, a group of plants comprising several relatively similar species. Identifying a plant species first with such a larger group, and then distinguishing it from the other members of the same genus, greatly simplified the designation of an individual species. Communication among early European botanists was also facilitated by their custom of writing scholarly works in Latin, so that, although plants were native to different parts of the world, their names were in a single, widely used language.

Prior to the publication of *Species Plantarum* by the Swedish botanist Linnaeus in 1753, the names of plants used in scholarly works were short descriptive phrases in Latin, intended to distinguish each species from others in the same genus. For example, the woodland sunflower, *Helianthus divaricatus*, a common species along RBG nature trails, was designated *Chrysanthemum virginianum repens, foliis asperis binatim sessilibus acuminatis* by Robert Morison in 1680. Successive authors freely amended the phrase-names used by their predecessors, to reflect new classifications, to distinguish previously known species from more recently discovered species or just to provide what the authors considered improvements.

The great contribution to scientific nomenclature made by Linnaeus in his *Species Plantarum* was originally conceived as a short form of the true scientific name, which remained in phrase form. For example, Linnaeus, who segregated the genus *Trillium* from the closely related genus *Paris*, designated the nodding trillium *Trillium flore pedunculato cernuo*, but in the margin, he provided the abbreviated name *Trillium erectum*. It soon became obvious that these abbreviated versions constituted much more practical scientific names than the increasingly cumbersome phrase-names to which they originally referred. Almost immediately, the binomial system of nomenclature, as it came to be called, became widely adopted among botanists using the Roman alphabet.

Binomial scientific names resemble most common names for species in that they consist of a noun designating the genus, combined with an adjective designating the species. All oaks are placed in the genus *Quercus*, and the species *Quercus alba*, *Quercus rubra*, and *Quercus muehlenbergii* are commonly called white oak, red oak, and chinquapin oak. Obviously, not all common names are direct translations of the Latin names; although "*cernuum*" does mean "nodding" and "*alba*" means "white," "*erectum*" does not mean "red," nor does "*muehlenbergii*," which honours an early Pennsylvania botanist, indicate any resemblance between this oak species and a chinquapin (a relative of the chestnut).

In a scientific binomial, the genus name, capitalized, comes first. Although the second word in a scientific binomial designates the species, it cannot be used by itself as the name of a species; just as referring to a plant as a "nodding" would not indicate whether one referred to a nodding trillium or a nodding onion, the adjective *cernuum* appears in the combination *Trillium cernuum* for the trillium, *Allium cernuum* for the onion, and in several other combinations as well.

Scientific names are used and valued by botanists for many reasons. They are "neutral"; Latin is acceptable to people who speak and write in many different modern languages. Also, because even an academic would not inadvertently slip into Latin nowadays, they seem to ensure that new scientific names are not coined accidentally in unlikely publications, or established by persons unfamiliar with the principles of botanical classification and the rules of nomenclature. Scientific names are only used in one sense, whereas the same common name may be applied to highly dissimilar, unrelated species. "Honeysuckle," for example, usually refers to the genus *Lonicera*, but in some regions it is a common name for the genus *Aquilegia*, otherwise known as columbine; "dusty miller" can be *Artemisia stelleriana*, *Lychnis coronaria*, or *Senecio bicolor*. A scientific binomial is clearly recognizable as the name of an individual species; "tall goldenrod," for example, could be a translated name for the species *Solidago altissima*, or might refer to a goldenrod of any species that happened to be tall, whereas the scientific name *Solidago altissima* is unambiguous in its application.

Like many other innovations, the concept of binomial scientific nomenclature did not arise instantaneously. Others, before Linnaeus, had at least explored similar ideas. It was Linnaeus, however, in his *Species Plantarum*, who developed the concept to the extent that the value of binomial nomenclature became widely recognized and its use became adopted by virtually all other botanists. He, moreover, put the concept into practice by providing binomials for all plants then known to European science. The enduring advantages to scientific communication are obvious as today about 250,000 species of flowering plants are known.

Iris laevigata

The masterpiece should appear as the flower to the painter - perfect in its bud as in its bloom, with no reason to explain its presence, no mission to fulfil - a joy to the artist, a delusion to the philanthropist, a puzzle to the botanist, an accident of sentiment and alliteration to the literary man.

James McNeill Whistler, 1834-1903
The Gentle Art of Making Enemies

Iris 'Edenite'

HERBACEOUS PERENNIALS

by Dennis Eveleigh,
Plant Records, RBG

A garden would seem incomplete without familiar flowers like peonies, daylilies, irises, shasta daisies, showy stonecrop and fall asters. These flowering favourites, along with hundreds of others, belong to a group called "herbaceous perennials" that dominate the garden from late spring through midsummer and again in early autumn.

While in the botanical sense a "perennial" is any plant that lives longer than two years, a "herbaceous perennial" is one that does not form wood in its stem and dies to the ground for part of the year. The underground survivor, a root, stem base (crown), thickened underground stem (rhizome), or bulb, sends up new growth the next season.

This characteristic of dying to ground level and lying dormant allows these plants to survive a difficult season. In most cases that season is a cold, snowy winter, but in some cases it is a hot, dry summer with the plant blooming during a cool, wet winter.

The herbaceous perennials brought together in gardens come from a wide range of different natural areas. They have been gathered over decades from the Northern Hemisphere. Habitat differences include variation in soil types, amount of seasonal rainfall and amount of sunlight. Diverse habitats include: rocky cliffs, meadows, woodlands, prairies, marshes, and stream sides.

Lupinus 'Russell Hybrid'

Today herbaceous perennials are utilized in various different garden situations including perennial border plantings, mixed plantings with shrubs, bulbs and annuals, and with low maintenance groundcovers. Since the late 1800's in England, perennials have traditionally been grown in "herbaceous perennial borders." This design concept originated during the Victorian era with William Robinson. He disliked the geometrically shaped "carpet beds" filled with greenhouse-grown annual or tender exotic plants in bright contrasting colours. He created a more naturalistic design involving a lawn "bordered" on the sides by planting beds. To add more permanence and continuity to the garden, he used herbaceous perennial plants. Until that time herbaceous perennials had been relegated to kitchen or cutting gardens.

The traditional herbaceous border, usually backed by a hedge, wall, or fence, was designed to be viewed from the front. These "borders" often were arranged in pairs facing one another with a grassed or gravel walkway between. Short plants were planted at the front with taller plants behind. In many cases the borders were designed to be effective during one season, providing a riot of colour over a relatively short period of time.

At the RBG, this one-sided border style is demonstrated in the Barbara Laking Heritage Garden within the Laking Garden. Intended to depict a southern Ontario garden between 1880 and 1920, this residential size garden includes a generous lawn bordered on three sides by one-sided herbaceous borders. Like the traditional herbaceous border these borders are backed by hedges or building walls and designed to be viewed from one side only. Herbaceous perennials grown in Ontario gardens at that period of time can be found in this garden.

In Norfolk, England, in the 1950's, Allan Bloom at Bressingham Gardens was one of the first people to promote yet another "new" perennial garden design concept called the "Island Bed." This design was similar to the Victorian era's rigid carpet beds in that the beds were designed to "float" out in a lawn area rather than border the lawn's edges. They differed from the Victorian beds in that they contained herbaceous perennials rather than annuals, and were groups of free-form beds with flowing curves. This design style employed the short plants at the edge with the tallest plants in the centre. A more naturalistic and informal setting was created using this design style. One could view each bed from all sides and look through one island bed to another, thus providing many enjoyable viewing points.

The RBG's main perennial collection within the Laking Garden is patterned after the newer "Island Bed" concept. The island beds were designed and planted in the mid-1970's by Dr. Leslie Laking and his wife Barbara. These beds, rather than providing colour for a short period of time, provide flowering interest from late April until mid October with the use of a wide array of perennials blooming at different times.

The use of restricted colour schemes in herbaceous borders was initiated and perfected by Gertrude Jekyll in England in the early 1900's. Several of the RBG's island beds in the Laking Garden display her fascinating colour exercise. Restricted colour schemes of blue\lavender\purple, white\grey\silver, red\pink\magenta and yellow\gold\copper are displayed in four of the island beds. This segregation of similar colours emphasizes the diversity within each colour range as well as highlighting the different textures and forms of the various plants.

A gardener's pleasure in herbaceous perennials is the anticipation of each perennial's bloom, the enjoyment when the flowers finally unfurl and their remembered beauty after the blossoms pass. While annual flowers provide a relatively static garden filled with colour, herbaceous perennials provide an ever-changing line-up of floral players that enter or exit the garden show each week throughout the growing season. Herbaceous perennials also add the bonus of returning each year to provide this constantly changing show of colour all over again.

Where'er you walk, cool gales shall fan the glade,
Trees, where you sit, shall crowd into a shade;
Where'er you tread, the blushing flow'rs shall rise
And all things flourish where you turn your eyes.

Alexander Pope, 1688-1744
Pastorals, Summer

Rhododendron Collection

Rhododendron 'Tintoretto' (facing page)

Rosa foetida 'Persiana' 'Persian yellow' rose (above and facing page)

The Hedge Collection

THE ARBORETUM

by Chris Graham,
Head of Horticulture and The Arboretum, RBG

Derived from the Latin *arbor* meaning "tree" and *etum* denoting "place," it is believed that the term *arboretum* was first used by English botanist J.C. Loudon in 1838 to describe that portion of a park used for growing trees. Today's arboreta also include among their collections shrubs and woody vines. By definition they differ from more inclusive "botanical gardens" by lacking the latter's herbaceous plant and glasshouse collections. The open green space and recreational opportunities they provide are increasingly important as the urban landscape continues to coalesce, but an arboretum is much more than a park. It is a cultural institution whose educational and scientific roles are demonstrated through documented, labelled and interpreted plant collections.

Plans to develop large tracts of land along the north shore of Cootes Paradise into the RBG's Arboretum date back to the early 1940's. The site however was first cultivated over a century earlier when William Rasberry cleared native stands of oak, beech and maple to make way for his farm. A fine stone silo of the era stands as a reminder of the land's former use. Sheltered by the Niagara Escarpment and with the moderating influences of Lake Ontario the native vegetation is one of the northernmost examples of the botanically diverse Carolinian Zone. This setting with its gently rolling topography was thought to be ideal for an arboretum. Its juxtaposition to Cootes Paradise with vast nature sanctuaries provided an opportunity for environmental and ecological study enjoyed by few kindred institutions. The first phase of development for the most accessible portion of the site called for a central grand parking circle with tree-lined avenues radiating from it, like spokes on a wheel. Each avenue was to feature trees with similar silhouettes - columnar, pyramidal, oval and so on and planted in matching pairs. Regrettably the soils native to the site are a nearly impervious red clay and most of the topsoil had been stripped from the land by a previous owner. In spite of extensive tile drainage systems and other efforts to enhance the soil conditions these combined conditions continue to present significant challenges and limitations on what plants can be grown. In time the notion of perfectly matched pairs of trees was abandoned though trees of like habit continue to be grouped. The crabapple, or *Malus* collection, was the first of significance to be planted in 1956. These plants have proved to be tolerant of the heavy soils and continue to thrive today. Other genera, such as *Sorbus* (mountain ash), have been less successful on the site but even this apparent failure has generated valuable information for future study.

The essence of any botanical garden or arboretum and the foundation for its educational, scientific and recreational programs are its documented plant collections. These are organised to create a living reference library of plants which may be appreciated differently. For some RBG visitors the arboretum is the venue for an enjoyable walk, for others it provides an opportunity to compare elements of the landscape, while for others it acts as a resource for taxonomic study.

There are many ways to effectively display and interpret plants - by genus, use, habitat, native range and so on depending on the primary message to be conveyed. Some collections like the Hedge Garden, first planted in 1962, are intensely maintained. Here visitors can compare the merits of over 120 formally trimmed hedges to determine which is right for their garden. Conversely the Native Tree and Shrub Collection is consciously cared for in a more natural way for gardeners who may want a gentler landscape. The 1.6 hectare Shrub Garden demonstrates the diversity of shrubs which will grow in southern Ontario. The plants are arranged alphabetically by genus, like a botanical dictionary, to facilitate study by researchers, professional growers and home owners alike. Flowering tree collections of magnolia, dogwood, redbud and cherry contain hundreds of specimens, each with its own unique charm and season while elsewhere on the site weeping trees lament their pendulous form.

Whether gleaned from expeditions to exotic shores or the product of plant breeders at home, new forms are always being evaluated in an effort to extend the botanical range of possibility with the ultimate goal of introducing to local horticulture plants of economic importance and garden merit.

Unlike institutions whose collections are comprised of inanimate objects the "living" collections of an arboretum do by definition change in the fourth dimension both cyclically with the seasons and linearly with time. Spring is heralded by golden forsythia and soft pink cherry blossoms. Sycamores and oaks afford a welcome escape from the heat of a July afternoon and in autumn maples are ablaze in scarlet and orange. The starkness of a magnolia silhouetted against a fresh January snow is balanced by its soft buds patiently awaiting the longer days of spring, thus completing the rhythm of the seasons.

While the beauty of the Arboretum should not be understated and its role as a tranquil refuge from the stress of the work-a-day world diminished, it is much more. It is a place of discovery, learning and science where we strive to understand and interpret our relationship with the botanical world.

Wisteria sinensis Chinese wisteria

Viburnum plicatum f. *tomentosum* 'Summer Snowflake' double-file viburnum (facing page)

IRIS COLLECTION

by Leslie Laking,
Retired Director (1954-1981), RBG

Irises are unsurpassed among herbaceous perennials in their capacity to produce a thrilling spectacle. Numerous iris species are native to many parts of the temperate world and others centred mainly in the Middle East. Their flowers are constructed of parts in sets of three but differ considerably in structure and color. Fascination with irises has prompted their employment as decoration or as an icon throughout history. The best known iris is the Tall Bearded which was cultivated in Europe as early as the 16th century. Tall Bearded Irises originated as natural hybrids from a cross between *I. pallida* and *I. variegata* discovered in the Italian Alps. Great strides in iris breeding were made in the 19th century which culminated with William Dykes, an English school teacher, publishing *The Genus Iris* (1913).

William J. Moffat, a Hamilton secondary school mathematics teacher and irisarian, was eager to support McQuesten's vision for a major Canadian botanical garden centred at the western tip of Lake Ontario. In 1945, he donated the nucleus of a Tall Bearded Iris collection knowing that it would bring quick results. This became the first feature plant collection at the RBG. The Spring Garden was already taking shape on the beautiful peninsula overlooking the quiet portion of Hamilton Harbour and by summer of 1948 was ready for irises.

Iris 'Dorothy Gee'

Fortunately at this time W.J. Moffat was serving a term as a regional director of the American Iris Society and through his contacts among fellow directors had access to most American commercial iris growers and breeders. After World War II, North American iris breeding was burgeoning, rapidly overtaking the lead held formerly by Britain and France, with keen interest centred on Tall Bearded Iris. The result was a steady stream of new cultivars from these American contacts. A good selection of historically-important irises was generously made available from existing collections at the Department of Horticulture, Ontario Agricultural College (now University of Guelph) and the Arboretum and Botanic Garden, Agriculture Canada, Ottawa.

Planning centred on the meaningful organization of the growing collection so that it would be more than a thrilling spectacle with its individual components appropriately labelled. The first concept was to plant a section demonstrating the evolution of trends in breeding Tall Bearded Iris through Dykes Memorial Medalists. The Dykes Memorial Medal is a British award available annually in France, Britain and North America when worthy candidates appear. The Dykes section became an historical collection presenting a picture of breeding trends among meritorious iris cultivars already singled out as superior through other awards programs. Also among the irises collected many had won the Award of Merit designation from the American Iris Society. In due course these formed the basis for a second concept to demonstrate in a broader fashion what happened as breeding of Tall Bearded Irises proceeded from decade to decade.

The newer cultivars mainly from U.S. breeders had evolved considerably from those of the 1920's and 1930's. The resulting decades section exhibited what had happened to flower form, colour and stalk throughout the decades. Flower form could be seen as becoming more stylish, narrow strap-shaped hanging "falls" (lower part of perianth) had become broader with an outward flare and often ornamented with ruffling. Other characteristics demonstrated in this array of cultivars centred on better flower substance, broader array of colours, usually much more vibrant and cleaner. The most significant new colour was what breeders flamboyantly described as "flamingo pink with tangerine beard." Reduction of greyed or tanned overlays and the virtual elimination of dark or muddy veining on the "haft" (upper shoulder of the falls) characterized the newer cultivars. Improved substance was readily recognized in the standards (upper parts of the perianth). Floppy gaping segments gave way to crisp arching standards, often delightfully ruffled, now recognized as hallmarks of any respectable Tall Bearded Iris cultivar.

Such characteristics, the manifestation of the principal objectives in breeding Tall Bearded Irises in the past half century, along with more abundant well displayed blooms on each stalk, could now be readily identified. As many of the cultivars were born and selected in much milder climates, it is important to demonstrate their viability and performance in our more severe climate. Canadian introductions, particularly in the Tall Bearded category occupying their own section, amply demonstrate their enduring desirable garden quality - floriferousness.

The Iris Collection in this garden, re-christened the Laking Garden in 1981, gradually broadened its scope to include such horticultural groups as siberian and spuria irises and representatives of dwarf and medium bearded categories. Species from the wild attract attention because of their diversity and charm rather than display potential.

The Canadian Iris Society has generously undertaken the responsibility for on-going infusion of new material to this already significant collection. The Iris Collection at the Laking Garden is far from static. Its vibrant nature beckons, and inherent instructional values therein encourage exploration and study always amid a veritable rainbow of colour.

Syringa vulgaris 'Dappled Dawn' lilac

Malus 'Hillieri' Hillier crab apple (facing page)

Hesperis matronalis Dame's rocket

Aquilegia 'Blue Shades' columbine (facing page)

Narcissus 'King Alfred' daffodil

Narcissus 'Peeping Tom' daffodil (facing page)

CENTENNIAL ROSE GARDEN

by George Pagowski,
Horticulturist, in charge of the Rose Collection, RBG

The Rose! Admired and cultivated since time immemorial, the subject of countless books and poems and celebrated in gardens created in her honour. Roses grow in the wild on every continent of the northern hemisphere. Fortunately, roses are quite variable in nature and they readily interbreed and mutate. Hence, plants showing desirable characteristics were brought under cultivation. Planted in gardens, perhaps in the company of cousins from other parts of the world, hybrids occurred. The showiest of such seedlings have been preserved and distributed.

Gardens devoted strictly to roses are a relatively modern phenomenon. In the middle ages, roses were grown in monastery gardens for their purported medicinal qualities and earlier, in Asia Minor, for the manufacture of perfumes (attar). The practise of growing plants for their ornamental value does not, however, belong to this century alone. Archaeological excavations of Knossos, Crete, suggest that ornamentals, including roses, were cultivated there 5,000 years ago. The Medes of ancient Persia probably cultivated the Persian yellow rose, *Rosa foetida* 'Persiana', which was depicted on tapestries and goldplate of that era. Unknown to western science, this rose was believed to be an imaginary flower. Apparently, a plant was discovered during excavations of temple ruins in Iran and introduced to western Europe in 1837. It is remarkable that this rose survived in obscurity for centuries. It has pretty, fully double yellow flowers, but seldom sets viable seed and its pollen is frequently infertile.

Rosa foetida 'Bicolor'
Austrian copper rose

By the mid 19th century, rose-breeding was quite active among roseophiles in Europe, especially France. Pernet-Ducher evidently worked some 30 years with 'Persian yellow' before introducing 'Soleil d'Or' which became the gene-parent of all yellow-flowered Hybrid Tea Roses. Similarly, the Austrian copper rose, *Rosa foetida* 'Bicolor', contributed its orange colour to modern hybrid roses. A planting demonstrates this historic development.

Indeed, the collection of Old Garden Roses, also called Antique or Heritage roses, is a living illustration of the development of garden roses, displayed in three large beds. Owing to climatic constraints, only cultivars known to be winter hardy were selected. One bed contains some quite ancient types, representing the Ancestor roses, such as *Rosa alba* and *Rosa gallica* cultivars, known to be in cultivation before 1500. Here will also be found roses of undocumented origin, featured in myth and legend. China roses, late 18th century introductions into Europe, are represented by their more winter-hardy offspring, the Hybrid Chinas, such as 'Hermosa'.

Another bed is planted with damask, centifolia and moss roses, cherished by 18th-19th century gardeners. Some of these roses could well have inhabited the grounds of Malmaison, where Empress Josephine Bonaparte established the world's first rose collection and engaged Pierre-Joseph Redouté to document it in paintings and engravings. Several of Redouté's roses are part of this planting, although visitors may experience some trouble in recognising their names owing to re-classification in light of recent research.

The third bed is devoted to examples of Bourbon and Hybrid Perpetuals, the garden roses of the 19th century. The first Bourbon roses are said to have appeared on the Ile de Bourbon (now Ile de Réunion), where roses brought by the colonists from Europe hybridized with China roses. These new types possessed larger, double flowers than heretofore known and stimulated vigorous breeding efforts. The recently introduced China roses transmitted their repeat-flowering habit to following generations, giving rise to a new class, the Hybrid Perpetuals. One of these 'Antoine Ducher' made a successful union with the 'Persian Yellow' rose and 'Soleil d'Or' was born in 1900.

The examples chosen for this living exhibit are believed to be the best from the past, particularly cultivars that caused some excitement when introduced or proved to be particularly good performers over the years.

The central part of the Centennial Rose Garden is used for the display of relatively recent introductions of Large-flowered (i.e. Hybrid Tea) and Cluster-flowered (Floribunda) roses. These cultivars were selected from the best performers in our trial beds. Here, the work of currently active rose breeders from around the world can be examined.

The rose collections are given to innovation. David Austin's "English Roses" were introduced after having been grown on trial for some seasons. Austin described his creations as "new roses in the old tradition." This new race is the result of hybridizing modern cultivars with Old Garden Roses. They possess the charm and fragrance associated with Old Garden Roses and new, bright colours of the Hybrid Tea and Floribunda.

The collections not only illustrate the development of garden roses, but are a potential inspiration to garden makers. One will find Miniature roses to furnish a balcony, ground-hugging types, dwarf and tall bushes for various situations, winter-hardy roses and kinds that require a trellis or wall for support.

A rose will always be a rose.

I take great pains to know the phenomena of the spring, for instance,
thinking that I have the entire poem, and then, to my chagrin,
I hear that it is but an imperfect copy that I possess and have read,
that my ancestors have torn out many of the first leaves and
grandest passages....

Henry David Thoreau, 1817-1862
Journal, 1856

Cornus florida flowering dogwood

WILDERNESS CONSERVATION

by Steve Bowen,
Teacher and Naturalist, RBG

Standing in the midst of a dark alien forest, huge trees stretching upwards all around you into a thick leafy canopy, you feel out of place. In every direction you are greeted by trees as far as the eye can see. Strange, unsettling sounds assail your ears. You do not feel a part of this environment, but rather an unwelcome intruder into it. Imagine what that would be like. So it must have been for the early settlers who arrived in Canada centuries ago - people who came here to start a new life and build a home for their families. To them, wilderness was something to be conquered, to be subdued, to be civilized. The very idea of conservation was a long way from seeing life, and the people set about changing the landscape with little concern for the impact it would have on the native species living there. As trees fell and the wildlife adjusted their range to avoid contact with man, few gave much thought to the overall impact this would have on the natural balance of the ecosystem. As farms grew and settlements expanded, few worried about how the dwindling natural areas would be able to sustain the increasing concentration of wildlife growing dependent upon them. The ruling philosophy was to exploit and control, and man seemed to lose touch with that part of himself that needed a link to the natural world. It really was not until people had reached a better lifestyle, did not have to struggle from day to day against the elements, that we began looking at what was happening in the natural world around us. We started to realize some species were becoming dangerously scarce, while others were gone. It was then that individuals like Henry Thoreau, Aldo Leopold and

Solidago canadensis
Canada goldenrod

Rachel Carson began pointing out a need to get back to nature and to use our resources wisely. We were, in fact, dependent upon it, not separate from it.

It is now well known that in any system, the greater the diversity, the more stable it will be, since all things are truly interdependent, forming intricate food webs with many interconnected links. In altering large tracts of wilderness areas and replacing them with less diverse cultivated fields and settlements, man upset this dynamic equilibrium. However, nature abhors a vacuum, and is often able to rebalance itself. As the loss of forest habitat forced moose and wolves north, deer and fox moved in to the new habitat for which they were adapted. Introduced plants such as catnip, dandelions, and some thistles quickly found a home on land once forested and covered in trilliums and trout lily. Eastern bluebirds gave way to starlings and house sparrows. Yet even nature has limits to what it can tolerate. If changes happen too quickly or are too severe, the equilibrium is lost and problems occur. With no large predators to control them, white-tailed deer populations have grown to such numbers as to be labelled pests in some areas. Purple loosestrife and zebra mussels, both introduced species lacking significant predators in North America, now threaten many of our aquatic habitats. Such occurrences showed that a conservation ethic was needed. As a result, numerous parks and reserves have been set aside to ensure homes for the dwindling species of wildlife, with the hope of helping nature regain its balance.

Today, sites such as the RBG play a key role in assisting with the conservation movement. Many are surprised that a natural experience can be enjoyed so close to a major urban centre. Providing this opportunity is not without its challenges, however. The Gardens must balance the desire to let people experience a variety of habitats with the need to limit the human impact on the wild residents. Thus, trails that duplicate an experience are closed off, and canoe explorations are restricted to non-nesting seasons. Intrusion of our wild neighbours into the garden areas must also be tolerated, as deer like to sample the various trees and shrubs on display and raccoons cannot resist the temptation of garbage can leftovers. Management of Cootes Paradise back to a viable marsh environment is still another commitment towards conservation.

While the RBG cannot offer much to the larger animals that once roamed our land - black bear, caribou, moose, and mountain lion, we do provide a valuable sanctuary to a host of smaller mammals, insects, birds, and wildflowers. For many people, this is the only "wilderness" experience they will ever have. For others, just knowing a place exists where wildlife can seek refuge is satisfying in itself. While it may not be pristine wilderness, it is hoped Thoreau or Leopold would be happy roaming the trails, content in knowing that their belief in a need for conservation was being addressed not just in the present, but for generations to come.

Helianthus divaricatus woodland sunflower

Clematis 'Bee's Jubilee' (facing page)

Aster novae-angliae New England aster

Along the Bridle Nature Trail in autumn (facing page)

There is a magic about the spring - some power that revives half-dead hopes and faiths and thrills numbed souls with the elixir of new life. There is no age in spring - everybody seems young and joyful. Care is in abeyance for a little while and hearts throb with the instinct of immortality.

Lucy Maude Montgomery, 1874-1942
Letter to G.B. MacMillan, 1906

Tulipa cultivar single late tulip

Do not linger to gather flowers to keep them, but walk on, for flowers will keep themselves blooming all your way.

Rabindranath Tagore, 1861-1941
"Stray Birds"

Paeonia cultivar peonies (above and facing page)

Rosa 'The Yeoman'

Rosa 'Geranium' (facing page)

ASSOCIATED MEDICAL SERVICES MEDICINAL GARDEN

by Garry R. Watson,
Director, RBG

After the grandeur of the other gardens, there is a sense of mystery and intimate expectation upon entering the Medicinal Garden at the RBG, the smallest formal garden but the one with the most stories to tell. In a few square metres no less than sixteen different themes inextricably link plants and mankind through history. They are arranged in the mode of a botanical garden of the ages, one with an enveloping hedge and plots of simple shapes, each one yielding its story in succession like the chapters of a good novel, saving the medicines of today and the classic poisons till the end.

Botany and medicine have been synonymous for most of recorded time. The medicine man or shaman was always an accomplished botanist. There has always been, and still is, an aura of mysticism surrounding those who were both masters and servants of nature. Any description of the art of healing in the literature of early Babylon, India, China, Assyria, Egypt and Arabia includes mystical and often astrological aspects. Hippocrates, it is said, coined the word "physician" from the Greek *physis*, meaning nature, to separate pharmacy from sorcery.

Traditional Chinese herbal medicine is based on the use of a rich and diverse flora to treat the whole body in an effort to restore harmony and balance between the five elements of wood, fire, earth,

Chrysanthemum leucanthemum
ox-eye daisy

metal and water so as to let the body's natural healing mechanisms work more efficiently. This is complemented by the Taoist theory of the balance of opposites, "yin and yang." Many of our familiar garden plants, such as peony and chrysanthemum, originated as medicinal herbs in China.

The homeopathic borders illustrate theories of herbal medicine popular from 1500 to 1850. The most intriguing, and at times surprisingly accurate, is the Doctrine of Signatures which maintained that the outward appearance of a plant was a god-given indication of the ailment it would cure.

Explorers often travelled with knowledge of healing plants but found themselves reliant on the "savages" of new lands for help with unfamiliar flora. Aztec studies have yielded knowledge of over 1200 healing plants. Mexican Indians used psychoactive plants in magico-religious rituals. Unique arrow poisons used in Amazonian villages have led to modern muscle relaxants. In Peru coca, datura and ipecac were found as well as quinine from the bark of cinchona which has saved innumerable lives from malaria.

Individual beds are devoted to the examples of plants from which the most important active ingredients have been derived: alkaloids, therapeutic in small doses but often fatal otherwise - the best known being nicotine, strychnine, cocaine, quinine, morphine, caffeine and codeine; glycosides like digitoxin, active in heart medicine (although three species of digitalis are displayed with the poisonous plants), and salicin, the basis of aspirin; and essential oils from which arise the spectrum of olfactory and gustatory characteristics of so many plants.

The variety of plant parts from which natural medicines have been obtained is surprising. In addition to leaves and flowers, the following examples come from North American plants: sap (birch, aloe), bark (willow, black cherry), seeds (angelica, flax), fruit (hawthorn, mulberry, raspberry), wood (lignum vitae), nut (cola, palm), stem (bittersweet), resin (pine), straw (oats), tuber (hemp, curled dock), bulb (garlic), and roots (peony, Indian snakeroot). In some plants, certain parts are medicinal while others are poisonous. The time of harvest is critical to maximize the active ingredient and may coincide with maturity (periwinkle), with the degree of flowering (cowslip and Chinese pagoda tree), or even the time of day (morphine from opium poppy). The manner of preserving the medicinal material is also essential for best results.

Both ancient and modern herbals are cross referenced by plant source and use. A recent one has sections on headache, skin and hair, first aid, circulatory or digestive problems, nervous disorders, gynaecological problems and childbirth, the elderly, and ailments of children. Herbal remedies are prepared or administered as: infusions in oils, teas, decoctions (vigorous extractions), tinctures (steeped in alcohol), syrups, creams, ointments, inhalants, suppositories, powders, compresses (soaked in extracts) and poultices (of whole herbs), and formed in modern pills and capsules.

The World Health Organization places 80% of the world's population as dependant on traditional medicine involving plant materials. There is renewed interest in screening plants for clinical substances of use as pharmaceuticals and in natural medicine. Many serious diseases exist for which satisfactory cures remain to be found or developed. Despite advances in synthetic drugs, recent discoveries of great potential have come largely from species in tropical rain forests. Attention is shifting from the search for new wonder drugs to deep concern for conservation of known medicinal plants and preservation of biodiversity in plant-rich habitats everywhere.

The RBG's Medicinal Garden serves as a reminder of both the original Italian botanical gardens and the botanical origins of the bounty of today's medicines.

I went to the woods because I wished to live deliberately, to front only the essential facts of life, and see if I could not learn what it had to teach, and not, when I came to die, discover that I had not lived.

Henry David Thoreau, 1817-1862
Walden

Hepatica americana round-lobed hepatica

Along the Tollhouse Nature Trail in autumn

Papaver somniferum opium poppy

Papaver orientale 'Hercules'
oriental poppy (facing page)

NATURE SANCTUARIES

by Barbara McKean,
Nature Interpretation Co-ordinator, RBG

In natural terms, the march of time is measured in an endless progression of habitat. RBG's nature sanctuaries cover 1000 hectares lying in a five by eight kilometre area in the heart of urbanised southern Ontario. An incredible mélange of wild plants grow here, in old fields and orchards, woodlands of various ages and successional stages, wetlands, reforestation areas and even some old-growth forest. The interaction of topography, geomorphology and human history has set the stage by producing this variety of habitat types. Climate is ameliorated by our proximity to Lake Ontario, an effect enhanced by our location within the sheltering arms of the Niagara Escarpment. With a mean annual temperature of 8.5°C, the RBG lies near the northern limits of the Deciduous forest region, Ontario's most biodiverse landscape.

This location, in what is also known as the Carolinian life zone, lends a distinctly southern air to our woodlands. Local microclimate often enhances this effect, and nowhere is this more apparent than Cootes Paradise, the largest of our sanctuaries. Separated by less than a kilometre of wetland, the slopes of the north and south shores of Cootes Paradise feature remarkably distinct flora. A walk along the warm south-facing slopes of the north shore takes one through forests of various oak, hickory and walnut species characteristic of deciduous woods. The understorey includes such southern specialties as blue beech, sassafras, witch hazel and the delicate flowers of rue anemone. In contrast, south shore trails pass by hemlock, beech, Indian pipe and

Monotropa uniflora Indian pipe

Christmas fern usually reserved for northern mixed forests. These differences are especially evident in March. As south shore slopes shake off the last vestiges of snow, hepatica has already raised its woolly-stockinged stems from last year's north shore leaf litter. Spring comes twice to Cootes Paradise!

To gain a fuller perspective for the important role that RBG's natural areas play within a heavily populated area, you need only ascend the Bruce Trail from Cootes to Rock Chapel Sanctuary. A walk along the Escarpment Trail provides panoramic views of all our lands: an island of green against the urban backdrop of Hamilton, Dundas and Burlington. Along the trail, the ancient limestone cliffs of the Niagara Escarpment sprout eastern white cedar trees that predate the arrival of European settlers in our area. Lying as they do within a UNESCO World Biosphere Reserve, they doubly reinforce the role we play in conservation and protection of native flora and its associated wild life and landscapes.

While woodlands adjacent to the Escarpment cliffs are dominated by a sugar maple bush their understorey is another matter. The rich, albeit thin, calcareous soil created by the Escarpment results in some species whose distribution can be traced to that thin limestone ribbon that crosses southern Ontario. Leaf cup and green violet are two such species, found growing below the cliffs on moist, moss-covered talus slopes.

This environment is echoed in our smallest nature sanctuary, the Berry Tract. Along with Escarpment woodlands, this property includes a large successional area that is rapidly reverting back to forest. The Berry Tract is indeed rich with the fruit of a diverse flora; a profusion of springtime blossoms on hawthorn, raspberry, apple and pear, results in an abundance of summer fruit (and an equal abundance of hungry deer!).

Hendrie Valley is a 100 hectare microcosm of Cootes, with south and north-facing slopes featuring distinct flora separated by the wetlands of Grindstone Creek. Sandy pockets on the south side of the valley feature soils that sprout silverrod and low sweet blueberry - acid-loving plants in an otherwise calcareous world. The upper reaches of the valley are home to the giants - herbaceous plants that tower over trails along Grindstone Creek. The showy magenta blooms of Himalayan balsam mingle with the three metre high parasols of cow parsnip and the flower heads of giant ragweed.

Though our natural lands are home to nearly 1000 wild plant species, not all are native to this area. While some aliens share the scene with native trillium and bloodroot, the population of others has skyrocketed, often at the expense of native plants. While "a plant is a plant is a plant" in photosynthetic terms, all things are not created equal in all ecological functions. Invasive aliens are generally competitive, opportunistic, prolific, tolerant of a wide variety of conditions and have few diseases or pests to control their numbers. They decrease biodiversity by out-competing native plants; often the very species that wild life depend upon. While purple loosestrife has gained a foothold in our marshes, garlic mustard and swallowwort are working their way through our woodlands. No one knows just why the scales of competitive advantage have been tipped in their favour in recent years, but speculation includes slight climatic changes and selective grazing of native material by our large deer population. Native species are known to run amok as well: touch-me-not is also spreading rapidly and usurping the habitat of other native wildflowers, perhaps I think, aided and abetted by our thousands of visiting school children who take great delight in its explosive seed pods!

This issue highlights some of the delicate balancing involved in managing people, plants and wildlife in an urban nature sanctuary. We ask visitors to imagine what their home would look like if over 100,000 people visited each year, reminding them that they are indeed a visitor in someone else's home. Educating people about our wild side is the key to maintaining it as a sanctuary for nature.

Don't wait for tomorrow;
Live now, and gather the roses of life this very day.

Pierre de Ronsard, 1524-1585
Sonnets for Hélène

Rosa 'Lordly Oberon'

Lily Collection

Lilium 'Joanna' (facing page)

Along the Brackenbrae Nature Trail in autumn

Along the Brackenbrae Nature Trail in winter

Cootes Paradise in spring

Impatiens capensis spotted touch-me-not (facing page)

If you have two loaves of bread, sell one and buy a lily.

Ancient Chinese proverb

Lilium 'Zephyr'

KATIE OSBORNE LILAC COLLECTION

by Charles Holetich,
International Lilac Authority, RBG

Lilacs are native to Central and South Europe and Asia, but are especially popular with peoples inhabiting the temperate regions of the northern hemisphere, who have been enchanted by the early spring blooms announcing the arrival of a warmer season, their fragrance and ease of cultivation. Early settlers from Europe introduced them to North America, where they naturalized and often formed groves of almost pure stands. In Asia, native lilacs can be found as far west as Afghanistan and as far east as Japan. However, by far the greatest numbers are found in China. At present, western literature recognizes 23 species of lilacs in the world.

All lilacs are shrubs or small trees, with the exception of *Syringa reticulata* and *S. pekinensis*, which are substantial trees reaching heights up to 15 metres. The majority of lilac species are very local in their distribution, but there are exceptions such as *S. reticulata*, *S. pekinensis* and *S. oblata*. *S. oblata*, found from northern China to Korea, most resembles the common lilac (*S. vulgaris*) in the shape of its foliage and habit of growth.

Some lilac species have cut leaves, while others have compound foliage. Some leaves are narrow and elongated like the leaves of the privet, while others have oval foliage ranging in size from 2.5 cm (like a boxwood) to 23 cm in length. Some lilac species grow at lower altitudes while others at elevations up to 3,000 metres. The Katie Osborne Lilac Collection, the world's largest, compresses into one hectare lilacs from diverse latitudes, longitudes and elevations.

China is a vast country and travel through it is very difficult and slow. For these reasons, the precise geographic distribution of some lilac species may still be in doubt and further exploration is needed. However, plantsmen and botanists have made journeys to various parts of China, beginning as early as 1742, and brought with them seeds or small plants for botanic gardens and courtyards of the nobility. They were highly prized and later clandestine efforts resulted in lilacs finding their way to commercial nurseries and universities where the first cross-hybridizations took place. Most cross-hybridizations are controlled, but they also occur in nature through a process known as "open pollination."

Cross-hybridization of lilacs commenced on a larger scale toward the end of the 19th century. For more than 75 years, three generations of the family Lemoine in Nancy, France, carried out extensive cross-hybridization experiments. This family produced superior cultivars, unique in size of florets and inflorescences and greatly expanded the variety of colours. They produced florets with double, triple and quadruple layers of corolla. Subsequently, extensive contributions in cross-hybridizing lilacs by Russian, Ukrainian, Polish, Dutch, American and Canadian fanciers have generated more than 2,000 recognized cultivars. Of the more than 1500 current cultivars in the world, the Katie Osborne Lilac Collection has more than 800 different cultivars.

The Katie Osborne Lilac Collection features the best cultivars of all the notable hybridizers planted about three to four metres apart on verdant grassy slopes. Blossoms may be observed as early as May 12th and the late blooming cultivars can occur as late as July 10th. However, the majority of the blossoms occur between May 20th and June 5th.

The optimum location for lilacs is an open, sunny location, well drained with a neutral or slightly alkaline loamy soil. The flowering buds are formed during the summer for next year's blossoms. As a consequence, pruning should be done immediately after the blooming period is over and the petals start to brown. The object of pruning and rejuvenation is to create an ideal lilac with 7 to 12 stems of different thickness or age positioned so that the growth of one stem does not interfere with the growth of another. The ideal height of the lilac shrub varies between 1.8 and 2.8 metres at maturity. It should be remembered that sometimes it takes three to five years to create the ideal lilac.

When pruning a lilac, there are four basic steps: removal of dead, weak or superfluous wood; removal of one of any two branches that rub each other; removal of cross-branches; and shortening and thinning branches. As the lilac plant grows older, stems 10 centimetres in diameter or thicker should be removed at the rate of one or two per year, preferably at the ground level or as low as possible. Pruning will encourage the vigour of the growth of the lilac and better flowers, leaves and stems. Better quality blooms are produced on stems 2.5-6.5 centimetres in diameter than on thicker ones. Stems with fewer clusters will produce larger inflorescences.

As one walks through the Katie Osborne Lilac Collection, one can recognize why the fragrance of lilacs has been appreciated since their discovery. Observation at close range will reveal single or double florets. There are white, violet, blue, lilac, pink, magenta, purple or yellow florets and even mixed combinations of these colours. Three cultivars of special note are 'Sensation', with its purple-coloured petals and white margins, 'Krasavitsa Moskvy', with its large creamy white four-layered florets and 'Dappled Dawn', with its variegated foliage.

At the 19th Horticultural Congress in 1974, the RBG was appointed to assume responsibility for the International Register for lilacs. Today, the Katie Osborne Lilac Collection and its records are the primary source of information, advice and propagating material for other lilac collections in Australia, Japan, England, Italy, Hungary and numerous places in the USA and Canada.

Lobelia siphilitica great lobelia

Eupatorium maculatum
spotted Joe-Pye weed (facing page)

And this our life, exempt from public haunt,
Finds tongues in trees, books in running brooks,
Sermons in stones, and good in everything.

William Shakespeare, 1564-1616
As You Like It

Along the Tollhouse Nature Trail in autumn

Along the Brackenbrae Nature Trail in spring

Hesperis matronalis Dame's rocket (facing page)

Trifolium pratense red clover

Viburnum opulus guelder-rose viburnum (facing page)

Tickle it with a hoe and it will laugh into a harvest.

Old English Proverb

It may fairly be said of me that in this book I have done no more than to weave a garland of flowers that others have planted, but I have tried to provide a thread that binds them together....

Michel Eyquem de Montaigne, 1533-1592
Essais

Prunus 'Accolade' cherry

AUTHOR'S NOTES

by Norman S. Track

How I see myself, how I see you, and how I see the world of nature, is a dynamic process that determines my perspective, vantage point and appetite for life. If that appetite weakens, my photographs turn pale. For to make a photograph is to savour life intensely, every fraction of a second. I wander in search of a bounty, seeking subjects at those special moments when the natural light is at its best, bringing back a harvest of images that live and speak for themselves, like songs without words.

We all have the same senses. We see, hear, smell, taste and touch. Why do we so often fail to respond to the natural environment? Have our senses become dulled, automatic, tyrannised by habit? Sometimes it seems to me that thought in itself clouds our perceptions, spinning a veil around them, obscuring what we see, so that we end up not portraying the world of nature but describing ourselves in the act of observation. In an ancient parable eight blind men describe an elephant. One grasps a leg, and says it is a tree. Another touches the trunk and says it is a snake. And so on. Ultimately, we all perceive differently and interpret our perceptions along unique, personal pathways.

Some years ago a friend of mine was excited by an exhibit of colour photographs taken by children eight years old. To him they presented a new perspective, yet it was one that he must have seen as a child. To reach that perspective was not a matter of kneeling down to the child's height but of rediscovering the wonder of the child's vision.

Along the Brackenbrae Nature Trail in winter

A garden is an ideal place to rediscover our spontaneity while learning about ourselves, about others, and about nature. In June the Laking Garden irises are a breathtaking sight. While photographing irises I saw some people look at the collection in amazement from the terrace steps, catch their breath and walk on. I saw others, after their initial amazement, walk among the beds for a closer examination. I remember one man on four consecutive mornings at seven-thirty walking briskly through the collection, pausing for a quick gaze at those that had just opened, greeting me, and then departing for another world - his office. Everyone visiting the Garden has a different, personal experience.

The natural world flows back and forth in a series of interconnected rhythms. In western countries we mimic the cyclical rhythm, as seen in the seasons, in our planting of gardens, both wild and cultivated. However a garden as we know it, as a beautiful cycle of floral exhibitions, is a cultural construct and our western way of conceiving and making a garden is not the only one.

When I lived in Japan I came to know a different kind of garden consisting only of stones and raked gravel. Such are the gardens of the Zen Buddhist temples and monasteries. The Ryōan-ji Temple, in Kyoto, contains one of the best known of these gardens. The verandah of the temple pavilion runs along one side of the garden with tile-covered clay walls enclosing the other three. In the late 15th century Sōami, a Japanese painter and garden designer, created this garden by positioning stones in a seven-five-three rhythm on a flat surface of raked gravel. This distribution on a flat surface, writes Irmtraud Schaarschmidt-Richter, "reminds one both in form and content of the *bokuseki* written by Zen priests, who similarly place written characters on an empty surface in such tensile relationships that the empty space appears to be filled."[1] Most visitors walk along the verandah, take

[1] Irmtraud Schaarschmidt-Richter, *Japanese Gardens*. New York, William Morrow & Co, 1979. p. 44.

several photographs and depart. Some visitors sit on the verandah, facing the garden, and meditate. Some experience the garden as a world with the continents in an ocean, others as a heavenly view of mountain peaks just visible through a blanket of clouds. There are an infinite number of experiences. In the autumn, there is a scattering of Japanese maple leaves and in the winter often a dusting of light snow. These are the only outward changes. The Zen Buddhist garden offers a quiet space in which the possibility exists for inner change through meditation.

During my travels in China I had the opportunity to visit another kind of garden, one that consists primarily of large stones and water. Since each season has its orientation, its lighting, its elements and its colour, each garden contains distinct, strategically positioned, stone groupings for each season. Spring stones are clear and slight and placed to be lit by the rising sun. The spectator is separated by water from the summer composition which stresses vertical lines and a full southern sun. Climbing in the mountains is the theme of the autumn formulation with steep, rocky slopes at their best in long shadows of the late afternoon. The winter configurations are modest in a sunless position in front of a white background, often a garden wall. Such encounters with natural phenomena are believed by Taoists to heighten spiritual awareness and enhance our ability to adjust the rhythm of life to the pulse of the cosmos until eventually the one merges into the other. "The spiritual legacy of Taoism," wrote Hwa Yol Jung, "is a spontaneous response to the plenitude and nuances of nature."[2]

By developing a greater awareness and appreciation of the world of nature we also gain greater insight into ourselves. This insight allows us to respect and respond to feelings and intuitions.

Photographing a garden and giving it new life on film is a reasonably

[2] Hwa Yol Jung, "The Splendor of the Wild: Zen and Aldo Leopold," *Atlantic Naturalist* 1974 : 29 (1), 5-11

straightforward exercise. All the material is within a confined area, the locations and blooming times are known. The challenge is to encounter every subject at the moment when the natural light is at its best. If it is not, then I accept that this was not the moment and I continue to search for that precise, particular moment.

INDEX

Dr. Track uses Pentax camera equipment (Spotmatic II bodies with fixed focal length SMC Takumar lenses and a Spotmeter V), a SLIK Grand Master Sports tripod and Kodachrome 25 Professional film.